There Was a Princess Long Ago

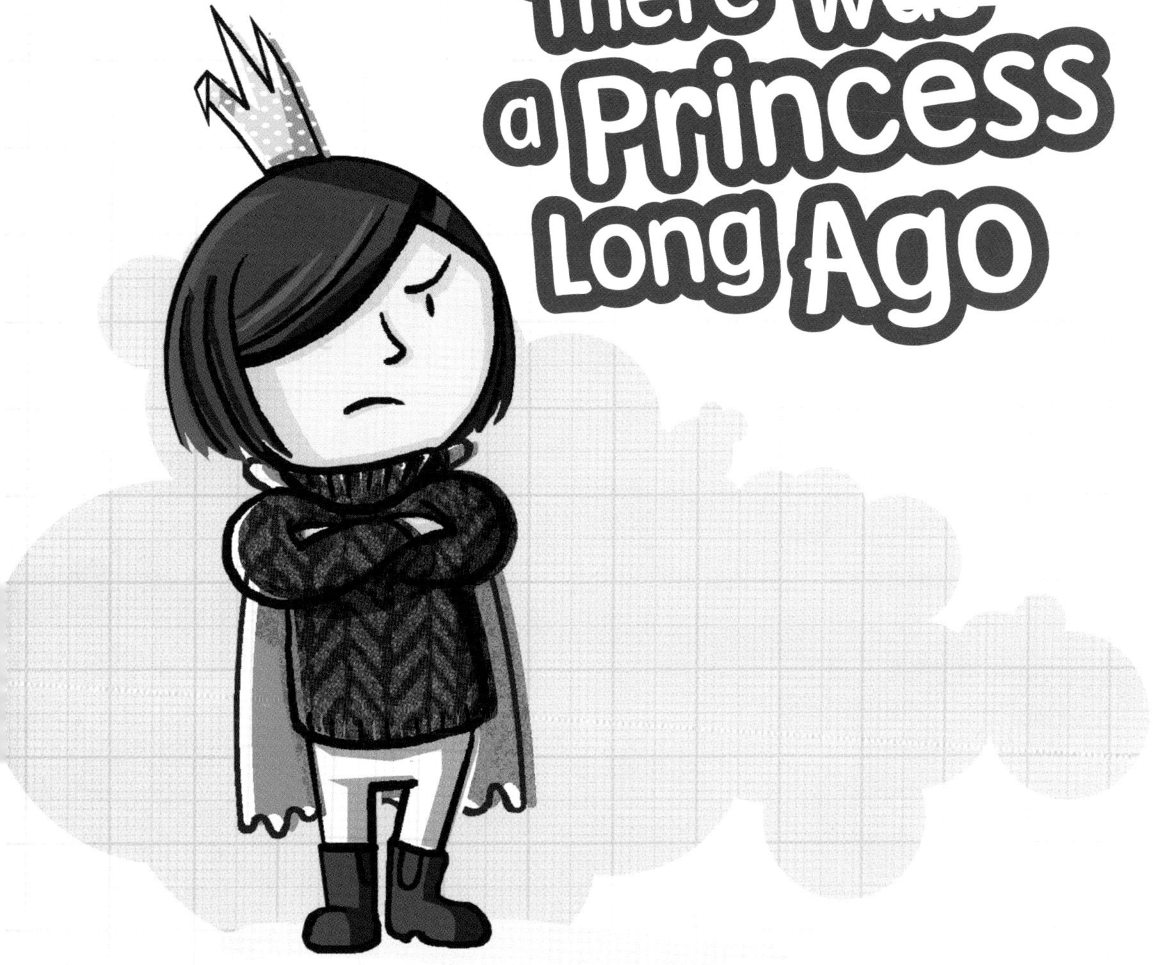

Story by Alison Hawes

Illustrated by Garry Parsons

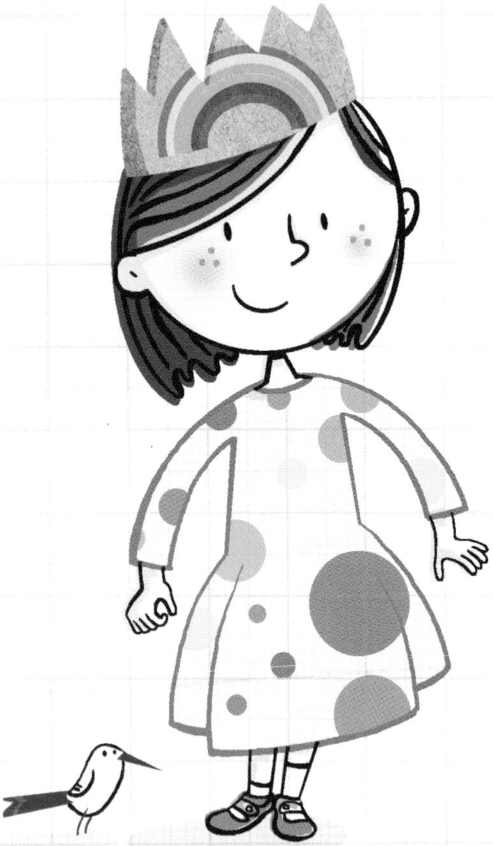

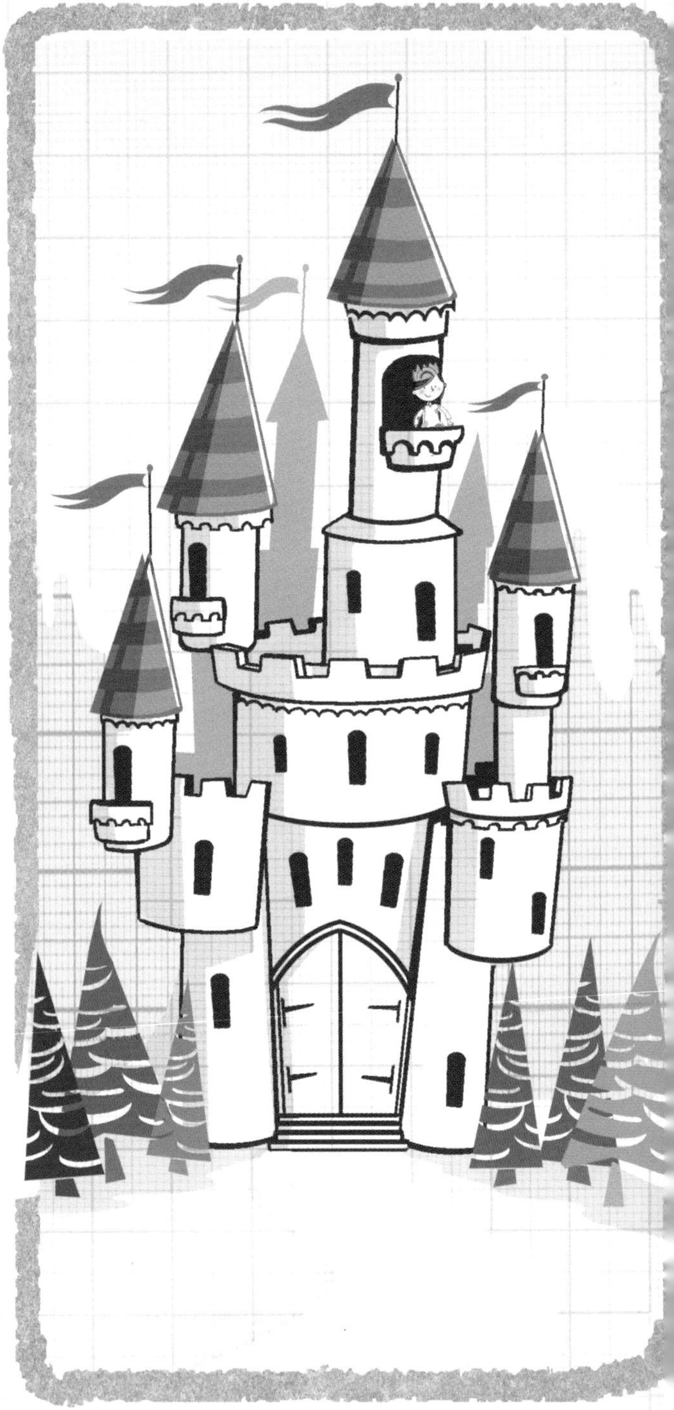

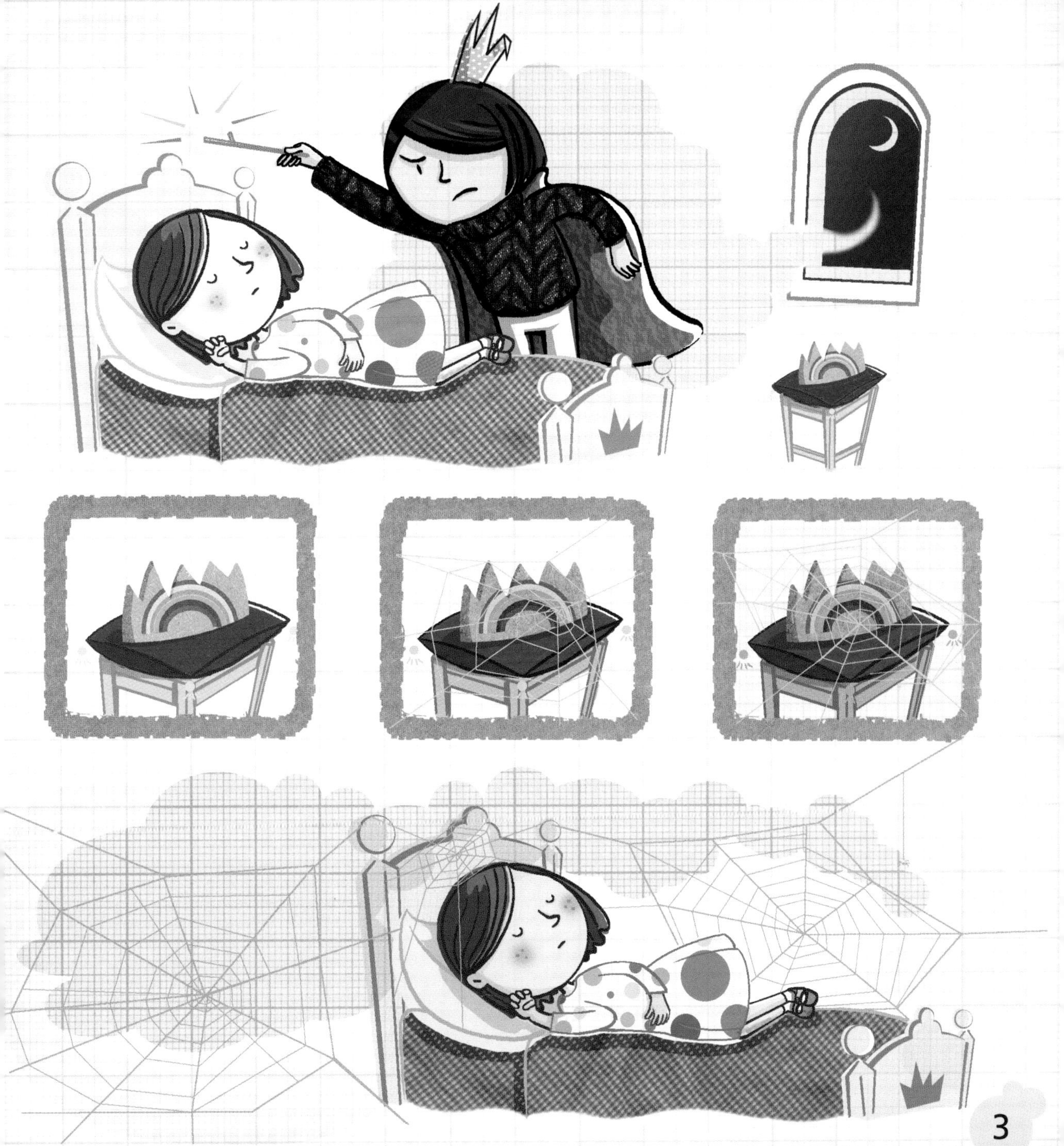

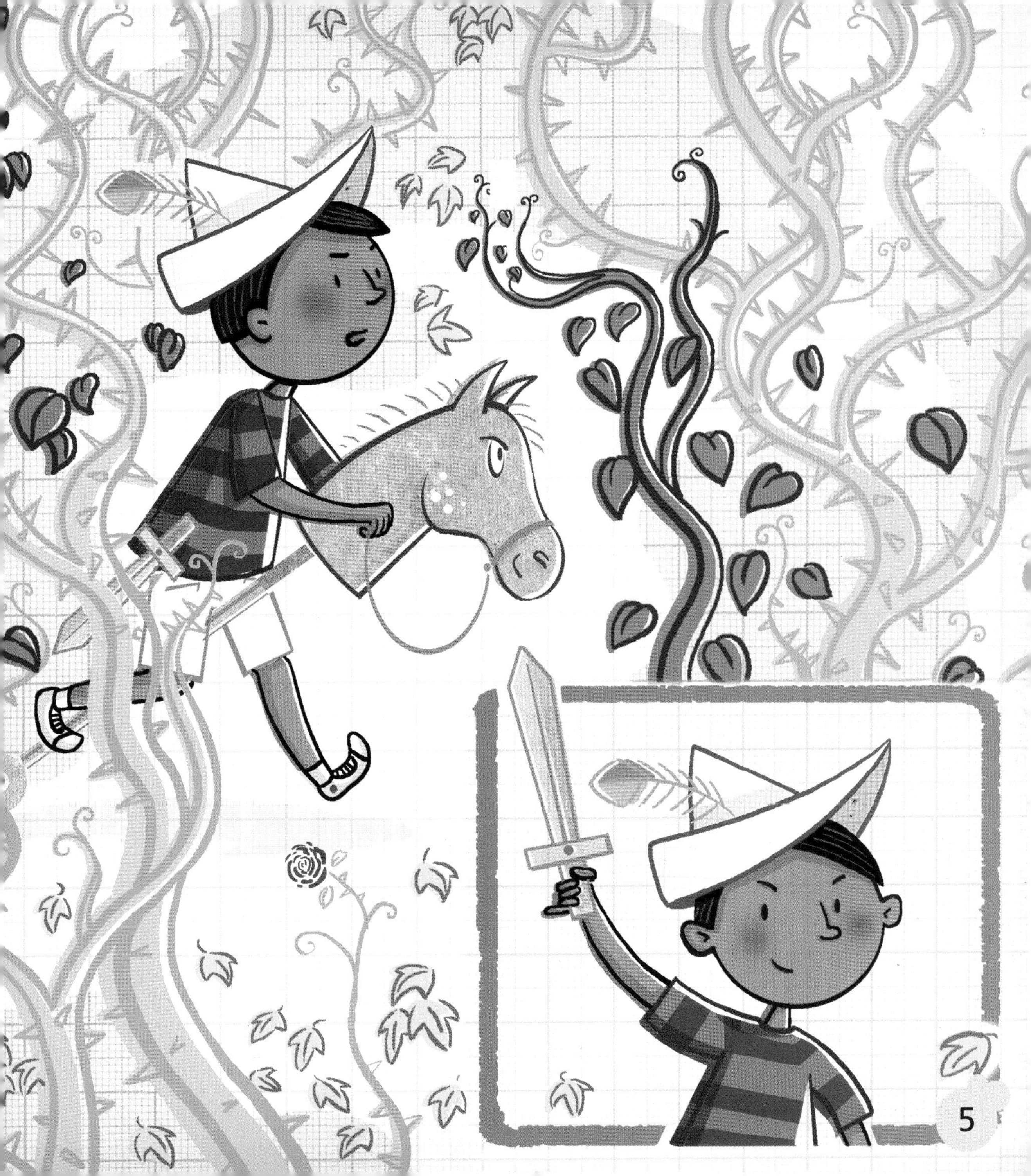

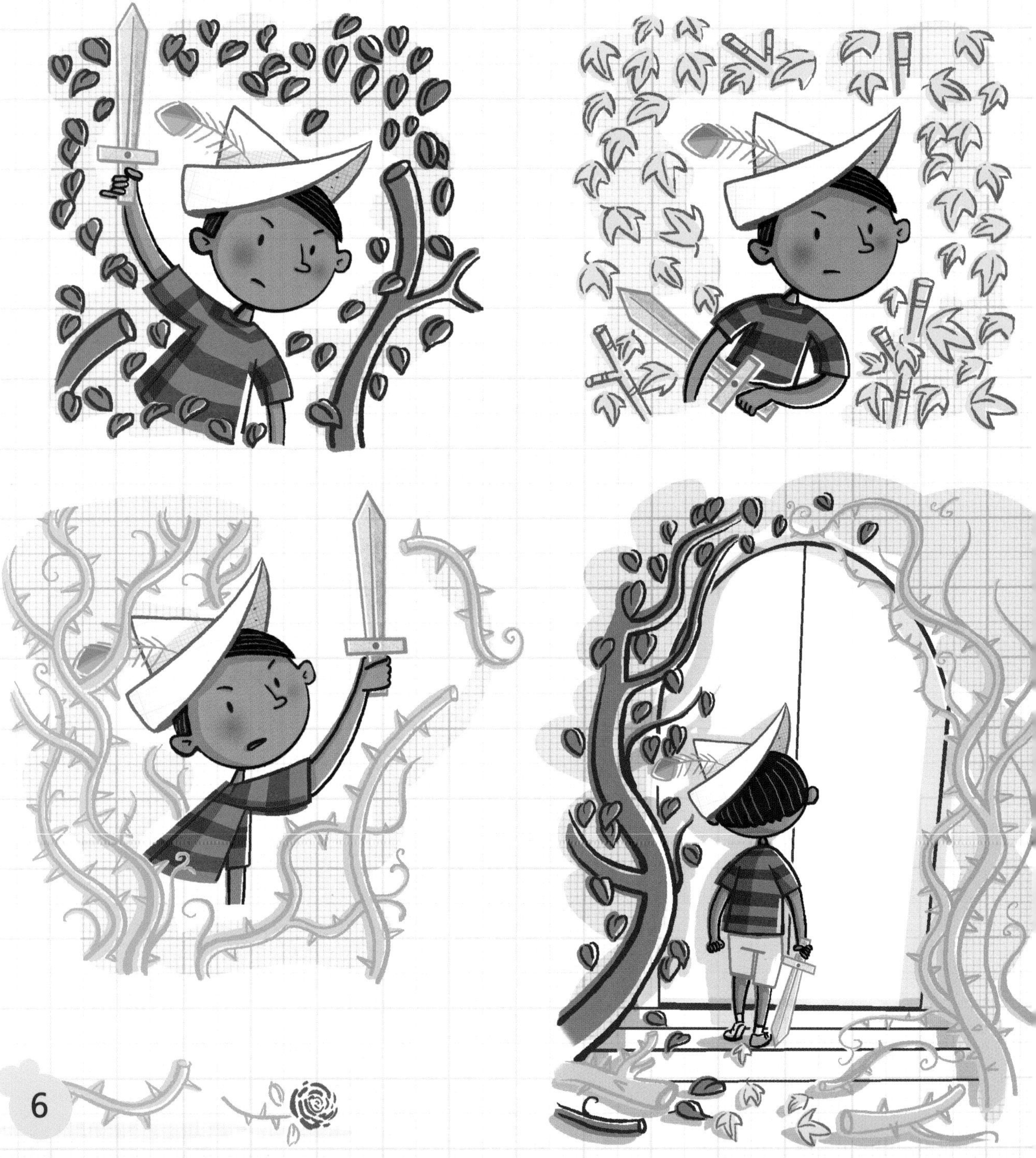

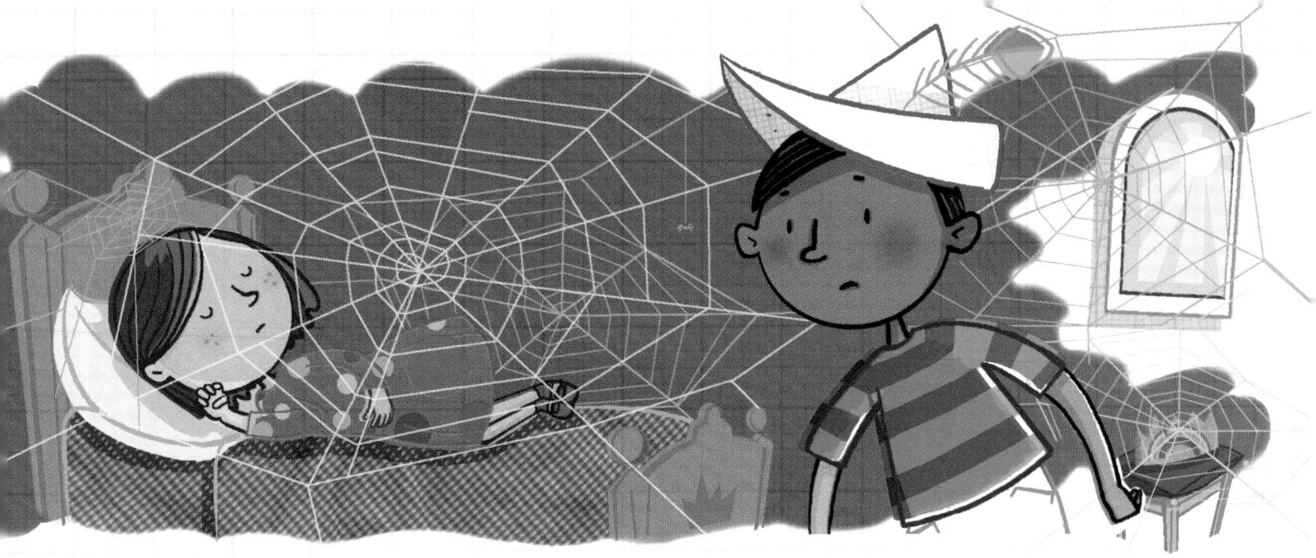

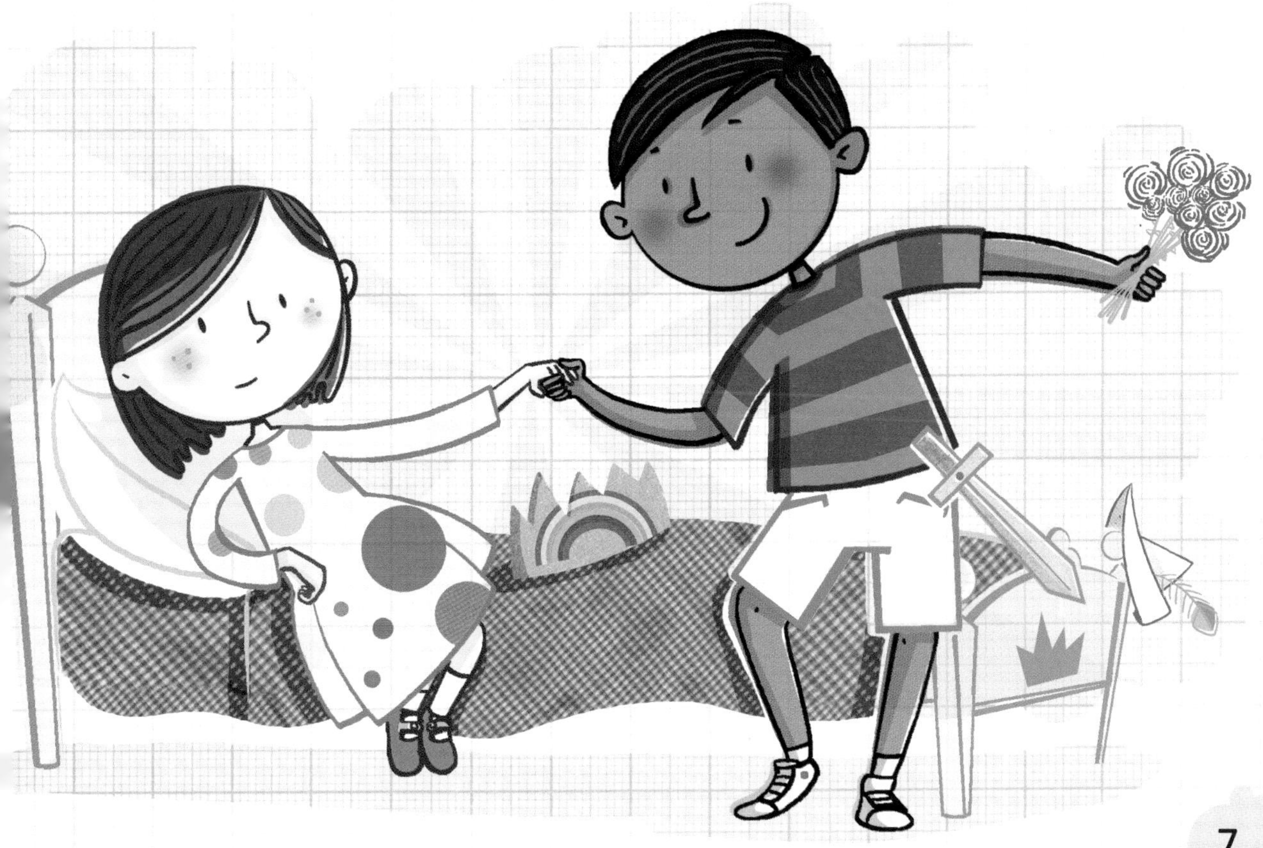

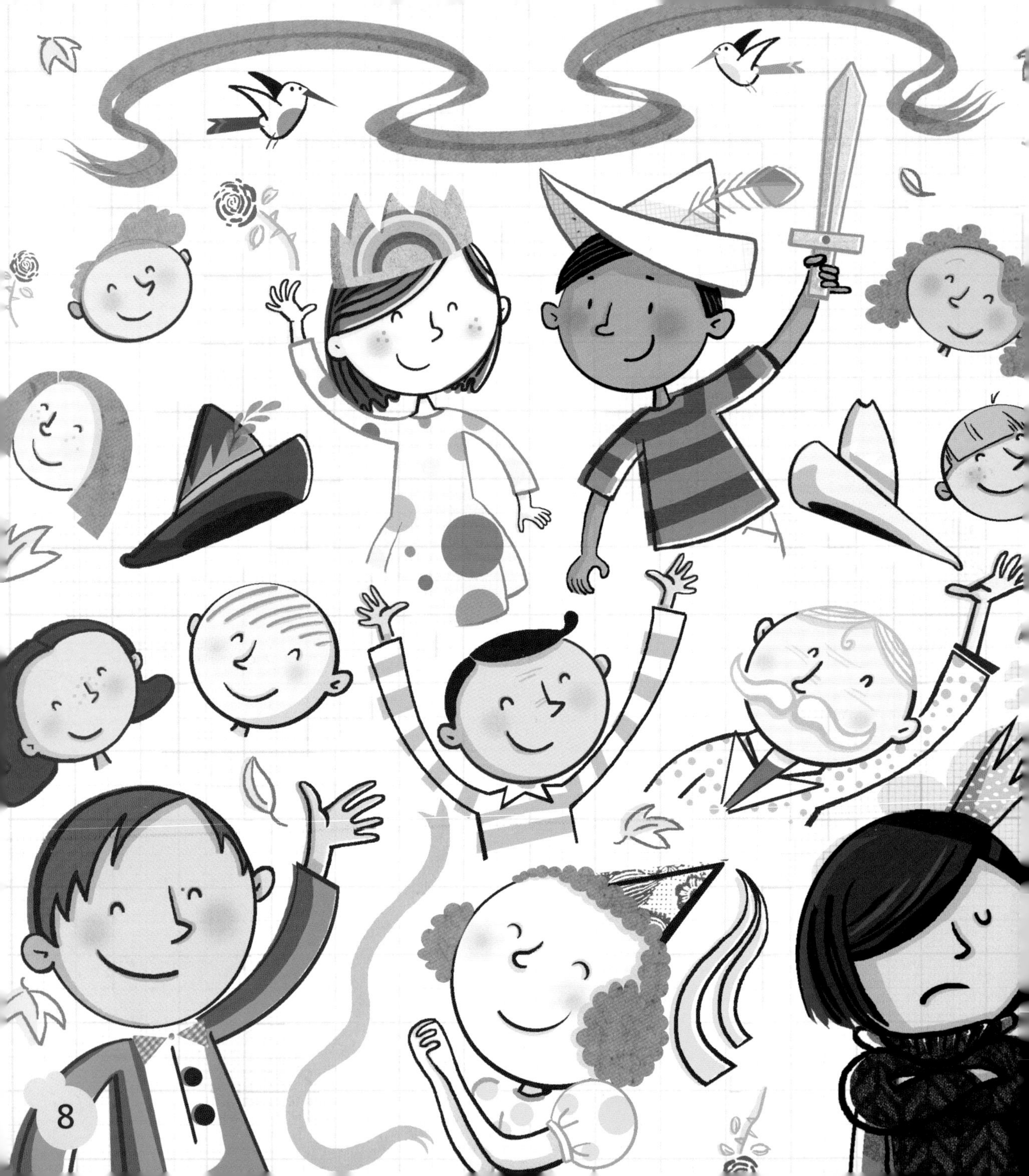